Self ♡ Care
PLANNER

Stacy Fisher-Gunn

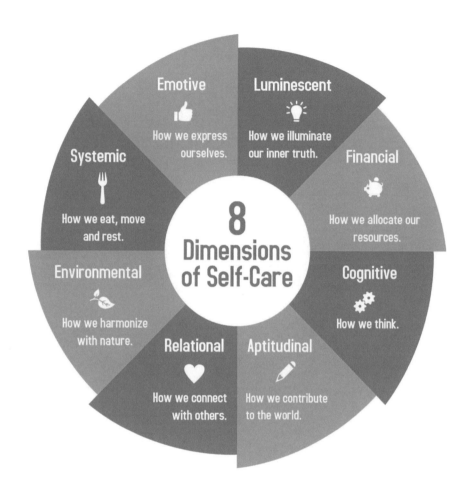

8
Dimensions
of Self-Care

Emotive — How we express ourselves.

Luminescent — How we illuminate our inner truth.

Financial — How we allocate our resources.

Cognitive — How we think.

Aptitudinal — How we contribute to the world.

Relational — How we connect with others.

Environmental — How we harmonize with nature.

Systemic — How we eat, move and rest.

LivingUpp

Published by Living Upp, LLC.   ISBN: 978-0-9974853-2-5   Created by Stacy Fisher-Gunn and Brenda Shecter

Contents

A note from Stacy

If planners and office supplies make you giddy, then you're in the right place.

For years I've been searching for the perfect planner to keep my hot mess of a life in order – one that provides just enough structure to keep me organized without cramping my style when it comes to creativity. But with each new planner came the eventual realization that something was missing. It was either too big, too heavy, too chintzy, or lacked a certain something that made me resume my search for yet another planner.

I desperately wanted something pretty but rugged, inspiring yet uncluttered, and most of all I wanted a planner that was effective at helping me manage my life – personally and professionally. Like many people these days, I use an online calendar to manage my appointments, so the hour by hour daily page wasn't necessary. But I did need something to help me organize my notes, create task lists, track goals, plan vacations, and jot down ideas as they came to me. Plus, I wanted everything to live in one place, fitting easily into my handbag. (Is that so much to ask?)

Because I've never encountered such a planner, I decided to design one myself.

You'll also notice that self-care is the central theme of this planner. That's because our health is our greatest asset. It's what enables us to achieve our goals and be in service to others. But I admit, sometimes it isn't easy to take care of ourselves. And that's why planning ahead and planting little seeds of self-care throughout the day is critical.

Living Upp's 8-dimensional self-care model will help you zoom out on your life so you can see the bigger picture.

Instead of wasting precious space with a lengthy set of instructions and inspiring quotes, we've included some helpful tips on our website at www.LivingUpp.com/Planner.

I hope this journal brings you as much joy as it has for me.

The 8 dimensions of self-care

S » SYSTEMIC How we eat, move and rest.

E » EMOTIVE How we express ourselves.

L » LUMINESCENT How we illuminate our inner truth.

F » FINANCIAL How we allocate our resources.

C » COGNITIVE How we think.

A » APTITUDINAL How we contribute to the world.

R » RELATIONAL How we connect with others.

E » ENVIRONMENTAL How we harmonize with nature.

How to rate your 8

Using a scale of 1 to 10
(with 10 being the highest),
rank how well you're
supporting yourself in each
dimension right now.
Don't overthink it; go with your gut.

Yearly Calendar

JANUARY

FEBRUARY

MARCH

APRIL

MAY

JUNE

JULY

AUGUST

SEPTEMBER

OCTOBER

NOVEMBER

DECEMBER

Year ....

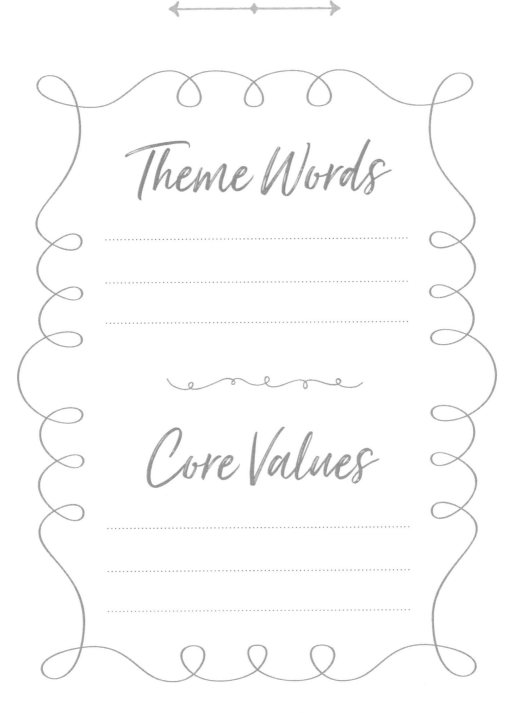

Theme Words

....

....

....

Core Values

....

....

....

8 Dimensional Plan

Systemic
....

Emotive
....

Luminescent
....

Financial
....

Cognitive
....

Aptitudinal
....

Relational
....

Environmental
....

Vision Board

Quarter ....

8 Dimensional Plan

Systemic ....

Emotive ....

Luminescent ....

Financial ....

Cognitive ....

Aptitudinal ....

Relational ....

Environmental ....

8 Dimensional Plan

Systemic ....

Emotive ....

Luminescent ....

Financial ....

Cognitive ....

Aptitudinal ....

Relational ....

Environmental ....

Quarter ....

8 Dimensional Plan

Systemic ....

Emotive ....

Luminescent ....

Financial ....

Cognitive ....

Aptitudinal ....

Relational ....

Environmental ....

Quarter ....

8 Dimensional Plan

Systemic
....

Emotive
....

Luminescent
....

Financial
....

Cognitive
....

Aptitudinal
....

Relational
....

Environmental
....

Month ....

8 Dimensional Plan

Systemic ....

Emotive ....

Luminescent ....

Financial ....

Cognitive ....

Aptitudinal ....

Relational ....

Environmental ....

Monthly Tracker

Activity	1	2	3	4	5	6	7	8	9	10	11	12	13	14	15	16
	17	18	19	20	21	22	23	24	25	26	27	28	29	30	31	
Activity	1	2	3	4	5	6	7	8	9	10	11	12	13	14	15	16
	17	18	19	20	21	22	23	24	25	26	27	28	29	30	31	
Activity	1	2	3	4	5	6	7	8	9	10	11	12	13	14	15	16
	17	18	19	20	21	22	23	24	25	26	27	28	29	30	31	
Activity	1	2	3	4	5	6	7	8	9	10	11	12	13	14	15	16
	17	18	19	20	21	22	23	24	25	26	27	28	29	30	31	

Monthly Calendar

MONDAY	TUESDAY	WEDNESDAY

Month

THURSDAY	FRIDAY	SATURDAY	SUNDAY

Month ....

8 Dimensional Plan

Systemic ....

Emotive ....

Luminescent ....

Financial ....

Cognitive ....

Aptitudinal ....

Relational ....

Environmental ....

Monthly Tracker

Activity	1	2	3	4	5	6	7	8	9	10	11	12	13	14	15	16
	17	18	19	20	21	22	23	24	25	26	27	28	29	30	31	
Activity	1	2	3	4	5	6	7	8	9	10	11	12	13	14	15	16
	17	18	19	20	21	22	23	24	25	26	27	28	29	30	31	
Activity	1	2	3	4	5	6	7	8	9	10	11	12	13	14	15	16
	17	18	19	20	21	22	23	24	25	26	27	28	29	30	31	
Activity	1	2	3	4	5	6	7	8	9	10	11	12	13	14	15	16
	17	18	19	20	21	22	23	24	25	26	27	28	29	30	31	

Monthly Calendar

MONDAY	TUESDAY	WEDNESDAY

Month

THURSDAY	FRIDAY	SATURDAY	SUNDAY

Month ....

8 Dimensional Plan

Systemic ....

Emotive ....

Luminescent ....

Financial ....

Cognitive ....

Aptitudinal ....

Relational ....

Environmental ....

Monthly Tracker

Activity	1	2	3	4	5	6	7	8	9	10	11	12	13	14	15	16
	17	18	19	20	21	22	23	24	25	26	27	28	29	30	31	
Activity	1	2	3	4	5	6	7	8	9	10	11	12	13	14	15	16
	17	18	19	20	21	22	23	24	25	26	27	28	29	30	31	
Activity	1	2	3	4	5	6	7	8	9	10	11	12	13	14	15	16
	17	18	19	20	21	22	23	24	25	26	27	28	29	30	31	
Activity	1	2	3	4	5	6	7	8	9	10	11	12	13	14	15	16
	17	18	19	20	21	22	23	24	25	26	27	28	29	30	31	

Monthly Calendar

MONDAY	TUESDAY	WEDNESDAY

Month

THURSDAY	FRIDAY	SATURDAY	SUNDAY

Month ....

8 Dimensional Plan

Systemic ....

Emotive ....

Luminescent ....

Financial ....

Cognitive ....

Aptitudinal ....

Relational ....

Environmental ....

Monthly Tracker

Activity	1	2	3	4	5	6	7	8	9	10	11	12	13	14	15	16
	17	18	19	20	21	22	23	24	25	26	27	28	29	30	31	
Activity	1	2	3	4	5	6	7	8	9	10	11	12	13	14	15	16
	17	18	19	20	21	22	23	24	25	26	27	28	29	30	31	
Activity	1	2	3	4	5	6	7	8	9	10	11	12	13	14	15	16
	17	18	19	20	21	22	23	24	25	26	27	28	29	30	31	
Activity	1	2	3	4	5	6	7	8	9	10	11	12	13	14	15	16
	17	18	19	20	21	22	23	24	25	26	27	28	29	30	31	

Monthly Calendar

MONDAY	TUESDAY	WEDNESDAY

Month

THURSDAY	FRIDAY	SATURDAY	SUNDAY

Month ....

8 Dimensional Plan

Systemic
....

Emotive
....

Luminescent
....

Financial
....

Cognitive
....

Aptitudinal
....

Relational
....

Environmental
....

Monthly Tracker

Activity	1	2	3	4	5	6	7	8	9	10	11	12	13	14	15	16
	17	18	19	20	21	22	23	24	25	26	27	28	29	30	31	
Activity	1	2	3	4	5	6	7	8	9	10	11	12	13	14	15	16
	17	18	19	20	21	22	23	24	25	26	27	28	29	30	31	
Activity	1	2	3	4	5	6	7	8	9	10	11	12	13	14	15	16
	17	18	19	20	21	22	23	24	25	26	27	28	29	30	31	
Activity	1	2	3	4	5	6	7	8	9	10	11	12	13	14	15	16
	17	18	19	20	21	22	23	24	25	26	27	28	29	30	31	

Monthly Calendar

MONDAY	TUESDAY	WEDNESDAY

Month

THURSDAY	FRIDAY	SATURDAY	SUNDAY

Month ....

8 Dimensional Plan

Systemic ....

Emotive ....

Luminescent ....

Financial ....

Cognitive ....

Aptitudinal ....

Relational ....

Environmental ....

Monthly Tracker

Activity	1	2	3	4	5	6	7	8	9	10	11	12	13	14	15	16
	17	18	19	20	21	22	23	24	25	26	27	28	29	30	31	
Activity	1	2	3	4	5	6	7	8	9	10	11	12	13	14	15	16
	17	18	19	20	21	22	23	24	25	26	27	28	29	30	31	
Activity	1	2	3	4	5	6	7	8	9	10	11	12	13	14	15	16
	17	18	19	20	21	22	23	24	25	26	27	28	29	30	31	
Activity	1	2	3	4	5	6	7	8	9	10	11	12	13	14	15	16
	17	18	19	20	21	22	23	24	25	26	27	28	29	30	31	

Monthly Calendar

MONDAY	TUESDAY	WEDNESDAY

Month

THURSDAY	FRIDAY	SATURDAY	SUNDAY

Month ....

8 Dimensional Plan

Systemic ....

Emotive ....

Luminescent ....

Financial ....

Cognitive ....

Aptitudinal ....

Relational ....

Environmental ....

Monthly Tracker

Activity	1	2	3	4	5	6	7	8	9	10	11	12	13	14	15	16
	17	18	19	20	21	22	23	24	25	26	27	28	29	30	31	
Activity	1	2	3	4	5	6	7	8	9	10	11	12	13	14	15	16
	17	18	19	20	21	22	23	24	25	26	27	28	29	30	31	
Activity	1	2	3	4	5	6	7	8	9	10	11	12	13	14	15	16
	17	18	19	20	21	22	23	24	25	26	27	28	29	30	31	
Activity	1	2	3	4	5	6	7	8	9	10	11	12	13	14	15	16
	17	18	19	20	21	22	23	24	25	26	27	28	29	30	31	

Monthly Calendar

MONDAY	TUESDAY	WEDNESDAY

Month

THURSDAY	FRIDAY	SATURDAY	SUNDAY

Month ....

8 Dimensional Plan

Systemic
....

Emotive
....

Luminescent
....

Financial
....

Cognitive
....

Aptitudinal
....

Relational
....

Environmental
....

Monthly Tracker

Activity	1	2	3	4	5	6	7	8	9	10	11	12	13	14	15	16
	17	18	19	20	21	22	23	24	25	26	27	28	29	30	31	
Activity	1	2	3	4	5	6	7	8	9	10	11	12	13	14	15	16
	17	18	19	20	21	22	23	24	25	26	27	28	29	30	31	
Activity	1	2	3	4	5	6	7	8	9	10	11	12	13	14	15	16
	17	18	19	20	21	22	23	24	25	26	27	28	29	30	31	
Activity	1	2	3	4	5	6	7	8	9	10	11	12	13	14	15	16
	17	18	19	20	21	22	23	24	25	26	27	28	29	30	31	

Monthly Calendar

MONDAY	TUESDAY	WEDNESDAY

Month

THURSDAY	FRIDAY	SATURDAY	SUNDAY

Month ....

8 Dimensional Plan

Systemic ....

Emotive ....

Luminescent ....

Financial ....

Cognitive ....

Aptitudinal ....

Relational ....

Environmental ....

Monthly Tracker

Activity	1	2	3	4	5	6	7	8	9	10	11	12	13	14	15	16
	17	18	19	20	21	22	23	24	25	26	27	28	29	30	31	
Activity	1	2	3	4	5	6	7	8	9	10	11	12	13	14	15	16
	17	18	19	20	21	22	23	24	25	26	27	28	29	30	31	
Activity	1	2	3	4	5	6	7	8	9	10	11	12	13	14	15	16
	17	18	19	20	21	22	23	24	25	26	27	28	29	30	31	
Activity	1	2	3	4	5	6	7	8	9	10	11	12	13	14	15	16
	17	18	19	20	21	22	23	24	25	26	27	28	29	30	31	

Monthly Calendar

MONDAY	TUESDAY	WEDNESDAY

Month

THURSDAY	FRIDAY	SATURDAY	SUNDAY

Month ....

8 Dimensional Plan

Systemic
....

Emotive
....

Luminescent
....

Financial
....

Cognitive
....

Aptitudinal
....

Relational
....

Environmental
....

Monthly Tracker

Activity	1	2	3	4	5	6	7	8	9	10	11	12	13	14	15	16
	17	18	19	20	21	22	23	24	25	26	27	28	29	30	31	
Activity	1	2	3	4	5	6	7	8	9	10	11	12	13	14	15	16
	17	18	19	20	21	22	23	24	25	26	27	28	29	30	31	
Activity	1	2	3	4	5	6	7	8	9	10	11	12	13	14	15	16
	17	18	19	20	21	22	23	24	25	26	27	28	29	30	31	
Activity	1	2	3	4	5	6	7	8	9	10	11	12	13	14	15	16
	17	18	19	20	21	22	23	24	25	26	27	28	29	30	31	

Monthly Calendar

MONDAY	TUESDAY	WEDNESDAY

Month

THURSDAY	FRIDAY	SATURDAY	SUNDAY

Month ....

8 Dimensional Plan

Systemic ....

Emotive ....

Luminescent ....

Financial ....

Cognitive ....

Aptitudinal ....

Relational ....

Environmental ....

Monthly Tracker

Activity	1	2	3	4	5	6	7	8	9	10	11	12	13	14	15	16
	17	18	19	20	21	22	23	24	25	26	27	28	29	30	31	
Activity	1	2	3	4	5	6	7	8	9	10	11	12	13	14	15	16
	17	18	19	20	21	22	23	24	25	26	27	28	29	30	31	
Activity	1	2	3	4	5	6	7	8	9	10	11	12	13	14	15	16
	17	18	19	20	21	22	23	24	25	26	27	28	29	30	31	
Activity	1	2	3	4	5	6	7	8	9	10	11	12	13	14	15	16
	17	18	19	20	21	22	23	24	25	26	27	28	29	30	31	

Monthly Calendar

MONDAY	TUESDAY	WEDNESDAY

Month

THURSDAY	FRIDAY	SATURDAY	SUNDAY

Month ....

8 Dimensional Plan

Systemic ....

Emotive ....

Luminescent ....

Financial ....

Cognitive ....

Aptitudinal ....

Relational ....

Environmental ....

Monthly Tracker

Activity	1	2	3	4	5	6	7	8	9	10	11	12	13	14	15	16
	17	18	19	20	21	22	23	24	25	26	27	28	29	30	31	
Activity	1	2	3	4	5	6	7	8	9	10	11	12	13	14	15	16
	17	18	19	20	21	22	23	24	25	26	27	28	29	30	31	
Activity	1	2	3	4	5	6	7	8	9	10	11	12	13	14	15	16
	17	18	19	20	21	22	23	24	25	26	27	28	29	30	31	
Activity	1	2	3	4	5	6	7	8	9	10	11	12	13	14	15	16
	17	18	19	20	21	22	23	24	25	26	27	28	29	30	31	

Monthly Calendar

MONDAY	TUESDAY	WEDNESDAY

Month

THURSDAY	FRIDAY	SATURDAY	SUNDAY

Weekly

	M		T		W	

Month ....

T		F		S	

Weekly

M		T		W	

Month ....

T	F	S
	S	

Weekly

⋙——→

M		T		W	

Month

T	F	S

	S	

Weekly

M		T		W	

Month ....

T	F	S

		S

Weekly

M		T		W	

Month ....

T	F	S

		S

Weekly

M		T		W	

Month...................................

T	F	S
		S

Weekly

M		T		W	

Month ....

T	F	S

	S	

Weekly

	M		T		W	

Month ....

T	F	S
		S

Weekly

M		T		W	

Month

T	F	S
	S	

Weekly

⋙⟶

M		T		W	

Month ....

T		F		S	
				S	

Weekly

	M		T		W	

Month

T	F	S

		S

Weekly

M	T	W

Month ....

T	F	S

Weekly

M		T		W	

Month ....

T	F	S
	S	

Weekly

M	T	W

-
-
-
-
-

Month...........................

T	F	S
		S

Weekly

M		T		W	

Month..................................

T		F		S	
			S		

Weekly

M	T	W

Month ....

T		F		S	

		S	

Weekly

M		T		W	

Month ....

T		F		S	

					S	

Weekly

M		T		W	

Month ....

T		F		S	

		S	

Weekly

>>>———→

M		T		W	

Month...................................

T		F		S	

S	

Weekly

M		T		W	

-
-
-
-
-

Month ....

T		F		S	
			S		

Weekly

M		T		W	

-
-
-
-
-

Month................................

T		F		S	
		S			

Weekly

M		T		W	

Month

T		F		S	
			S		

Weekly

»»———————›

M		T		W	

Month

T		F		S	
			S		

Weekly

M		T		W	

Month

T		F		S	

		S	

Weekly

M		T		W	

Month

T	F	S
	S	

Weekly

	M		T		W	

Month ....

T	F	S
		S

Weekly

M		T		W	

Month ....

T		F		S	
			S		

Weekly

M		T		W	

Month..............................

T		F		S	
			S		

Weekly

»»———→

M		T		W	

Month ....

T	F	S	

Weekly

M		T		W	

Month

T		F		S	

				S	

Weekly

M	T	W

Month

T	F	S

		S

Weekly

M		T		W	

Month ....

T	F	S

Weekly

M	T	W

Month..........................

T		F		S	

		S	

Weekly

M		T		W	

Month ....

T		F		S	
			S		

Weekly

M		T		W	

Month ....

T		F		S	
			S		

Weekly

»»→

M		T		W	

Month ....

T		F		S	
		S			

Weekly

M	T	W

Month

T	F	S

		S

Weekly

M		T		W	

Month ....

T	F	S

S

Weekly

M	T	W

Month

T	F	S
	S	

Weekly

»»——————→

M		T		W	

Month

T		F		S	

		S	

Weekly

	M		T		W	

-
-
-
-
-

Month ....

T		F		S	

			S	

Weekly

M		T		W	

Month

T	F	S

		S

Weekly

M		T		W	

Month ....

T	F	S

		S

Weekly

M		T		W	

Month

T		F		S	

S	

Weekly

M		T		W	

Month

T	F	S

		S

Weekly

M		T		W	

Month ....

T	F	S

		S

Weekly

M		T		W	

Month

T	F	S

		S	

Weekly

M		T		W	

Month ....

T		F		S	
		S			

Weekly

M		T		W	

Month

T	F	S	
		S	

Weekly

M		T		W	

Month......................

T		F		S	

Weekly

	M		T		W	

Month

T		F		S	

Weekly

M	T	W

Month ....

T		F		S	
			S		

Weekly

	M		T		W	

Month ....

T		F		S	

		S	

68634910R00107

Made in the USA
Lexington, KY
16 October 2017